D1391709

Alfred Pohler

# *Enchanting* **Alpine Flowers**

Verlag Lohmann — A-6433 Oetz, Tirol

Front cover:
Valuga Lechtaler Alps
Blue Monkshood and Alpine Ragwort

Back cover:
Martagon Lily in a field in the Komperdell

*All photographs, descriptions and drawings by the author*
*English translation: Jacqueline Schweighofer*

*Edition: 1985*
*All rights reserved.*
*Publisher: Verlag Lohmann, A-6433 Oetz, Tirol*
*Tel. 05252/6578 - Alpinadruck Innsbruck*
*Printed in Austria*

# FOREWORD

What would the Alps be without their floral decoration? All that delight at the sight of flower-carpeted meadows and rocks ablaze with colour would be missing. It is a particular gift of the Creator that enables us to comprehend all this enchanting beauty — a glimpse of paradise, as it were.

It is not merely the immeasurable variety and the riotous colour of these delightful specimens that is so fascinating; it is, too, their exemplary and frequently dramatic fight for survival which is so impressive.

The enormous efforts to secure propagation by a wide variety of shapes and by brilliant colours are indications of Nature's inventiveness and her inimitable technique. Even in our modern, highly technical world the pliancy and elasticity of such plant cells is incomparably perfect. Such magnificent feats arouse our boundless admiration.

It was our aim to provide a representative survey of all these colourful creations with their extravagant profusion of bloom. One hundred conspicuously flowering Alpine plants are pictured in colour, accompanied by brief botanical descriptions on the opposite page.

The survey is not arranged in any particular order; the plants are grouped according to colour and are alphabetically ordered. To make identification easier the whole plant is shown; since this can also be misleading, however, the normal height of the stem is given first in the description.

References to the size of flowers and leaves or the thickness of the stem are relative and apply to the particular plant described. Botanical terms are defined in the "Botany in brief" section. Coloured markings down the edge of the pages and the alphabetically ordered index of plants serve to facilitate the search. The book has been designed so as to be easily carried.

In awareness of the protection these exquisite plants require and knowing that they can only fully display their entire splendour in a natural environment, may it be the aim and the responsibility of all to preserve this magnificent world of Alpine flowers for as long as possible.

Reutte, 1985                                        Alfred Pohler

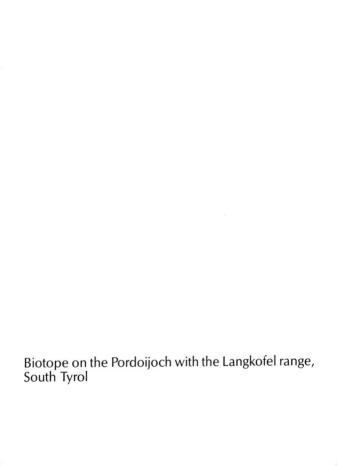

Biotope on the Pordoijoch with the Langkofel range, South Tyrol

# ALPINE ROSE

## Rhododendron ferrugineum

| | |
|---|---|
| **Family:** | Heather Family Ericaceae |
| **Shrub:** | 20—100 cm high, ramose, branches round, woody, brown-grey, bare, foliate, hardy |
| **Leaves:** | petiolate or sessile, lanceolate-elliptic, entire, green above, shiny, reddish-scaly beneath, young leaves green beneath, alternate, hardy |
| **Flowers:** | dense terminal clusters, funnel-shaped corolla — campanulate with five blunt lobes, bright red, a few white stamens, pleasant scent. Calyx 5-merous, pointed, accumbent, green |
| **Flowering time:** | June—August |
| **Habitat:** | 1500—3000 m, calcifuge soils rich in humus, mountain meadows, alpine pastures, heaths, scrubland, open woods, boulder terrain<br>Fairly frequent. Locally prolific |

**Distribution:** Alps, Pyrenees, northern Apennines

8

# CREEPING AZALEA

### Loiseleuria procumbens

| | |
|---|---|
| **Family:** | Heather Family Ericaceae |
| **Dwarf shrub:** | with prostrate, ramose branches, trunk up to 45 cm long, gnarled, woody, round, densely foliate |
| **Leaves:** | opposite, small, linear, margins rolled under, dark green, shiny, evergreen |
| **Flowers:** | terminal clusters, pink to dark red, 5-merous calyx, corolla light pink, campanulate, 5 lobes, ovate purplish red buds |
| **Flowering time:** | May—August |
| **Habitat:** | 1500—3000 m, avoids lime, overgrown ridges, rocky heaths, morainic slopes, schistose banks, mat-like or forming cushions. Frequent. |
| **Distribution:** | Alps |

# MUSK THISTLE

## Carduus nutans

**Family:** Daisy Family Compositae

**Stem:** 40—120 cm high, erect, sturdy, branching, green-grey, prickly foliate, shrub-like

**Leaves:** alternate, sessile, lanceolate, pointed, deeply pinnatifid, lobes irregularly spiny, stiff, leathery, decurrent, green-grey, long

**Flowers:** solitary terminal flower heads, 3—6 cm in diameter, nodding, disc florets only, purplish red; bracts lanceolate, pointed, spiny, green, turned back in full flower, tinged red

**Flowering time:** July—September

**Habitat:** up to 2000 m, stony ground, meadows, scree, scarps, sunny slopes, at edge of woods and thickets, wetlands. Infrequent.

**Distribution:** Alps, Pyrenees, Norway

# MELANCHOLY THISTLE

## Cirsium helenioides

| | |
|---|---|
| **Family:** | Daisy Family Compositae |
| **Stem:** | 40—120 cm high, erect, round, fluted, green foliate, tinged red, woolly |
| **Leaves:** | large, 20—40 cm long, 4—8 cm wide, toothed, pinnately-lobed, too, with sections turned upwards, white-woolly beneath, matt green above, alternate; top stem leaves narrow-lanceolate, entire, sessile |
| **Flowers:** | terminal, on long, vigorous stalks, one to three large flower heads, 3—4 cm in diameter, disc florets only, longer at edge, dark pink to purple; spherical involucre with dark brown scaly flower bracts |
| **Flowering time:** | July—August |
| **Habitat:** | up to 1700 m, moist soils, low in lime, banks of streams, wet, stony, mountain meadows, slopes, scrub areas, with Alpine roses, head-waters. Infrequent. Rare in calcareous districts. |

**Distribution:** Alps

# VULGAR THISTLE

## *Cirsium vulgare*

| | |
|---|---|
| **Family:** | Daisy Family Compositae |
| **Stem:** | 60—120 cm high, bush, usually branching, foliate, spiny winged, green, sturdy |
| **Leaves:** | alternate, deeply pinnately lobed, spiny, rough, cobwebby woolly beneath, side leaf tip bifid, lanceolate with long, strong spine at end, green, decurrent |
| **Flowers:** | solitary, terminal, occasionally two to three, large, 3—4 cm in diameter and 6—8 cm long, involucre ovate, disc florets only, dark pink or purple; very small, spiny flower bracts |
| **Flowering time:** | June—September |
| **Habitat:** | up to 1800 m, nitrogenous soils, at edge of woods and thickets, wetlands, pastures, stony meadows, clearings, at edge of paths. Frequent. |
| **Distribution:** | Alps, Pyrenees, Apennines, throughout Europe |

# GERMAN GENTIAN

## Gentianella germanica

**Family:**    Gentian Family Gentianaceae

**Stem:**    5—40 cm high, erect, slender, round, branching, foliate, green-brown

**Leaves:**    radical, spatulate to widely lanceolate, entire, parallel veined, green; stem leaves ovate-lanceolate, sessile, green, tinged brownish red

**Flowers:**    dense racemes, five petal lobes, ovate-pointed, violet to pink, more rarely white, throat bearded, calyx funnel-shaped to tubular; sepals lanceolate, pointed, flat, green-brown, petals spreading

**Flowering time:**    June—October

**Habitat:**    up to 2800 m, stony, poor soils, warm, stony slopes, mountain meadows, pastures, open moorland.
Scattered.

**Distribution:** Alps

| PROTECTED! |
|:---:|

# SPRING HEATH

## Erica herbacea

| | |
|---|---|
| **Family:** | Heather Family Ericaceae |
| **Stem:** | dwarf shrub, erect or ascending, thickly branched, twigs woody, slender, round, brown, foliate, up to 35 cm long |
| **Leaves:** | slim, linear, acicular, sessile, evergreen, leathery, frequently verticillate on twig, 6—7 mm long, bare, pointed |
| **Flowers:** | long clusters, turned to one side, usually terminal, corolla four-merous, bell-shaped to jug-shaped, pink or purple; sepals four-merous, same colour or darker, fleshy red, eight stamens, one style, flower on short stalk, nodding |
| **Flowering time:** | February—May |
| **Habitat:** | 600—2600 m, on stony, sunny soils, warm meadows, rocks, slopes, open woods, dwarf shrub heaths, wetlands, open pine woods.<br>Frequent, gregarious, cushions. |
| **Distribution:** | Alps, Apennines, Illyrian Mountains, Jura, Apuan Alps |

# ORANGE LILY
## Lilium bulbiferum

**Family:** Lily Family Liliaceae

**Stem:** 20—100 cm high, erect, strong, round, sulcate, green, foliate

**Leaves:** alternate, lanceolate to linear, entire, hairy, green; bulbils of up to pea-size in the leaf axils

**Flowers:** terminal, solitary, but up to five large flowers, too, six petals, ovate, pointed, bright orange, erect, frequently brown spotted; protruding stigma and brownish red stamens

**Flowering time:** June—July

**Habitat:** 800—1700 m, calcareous soils, screes, boulders, sunny mountain meadows, pastures, slopes.
Rare, completely absent in many areas.

**Distribution:** Alps (particularly Dolomites, southern Alps, maritime Alps, northern limestone Alps)

---

**PROTECTED!**

# CENTAUREA SCABIOSA

| | |
|---|---|
| **Family:** | Daisy Family Compositae |
| **Stem:** | 20—80 cm high, erect, sturdy, ramose, round-sulcate, green, foliate |
| **Leaves:** | alternate, sessile, pinnate, deeply notched, single lobes oblong-linear, pointed, green; lower stem leaves with short stalks, shiny |
| **Flowers:** | large, spherical heads, disc florets pink-violet to purple, marginal petals larger, pinnately split; spherical calyx, dense, widely lanceolate flower bracts, brown, villous |
| **Flowering time:** | July—September |
| **Habitat:** | 800—2400 m, various soils, meadows, edge of paths, pastures, with pines, slopes. Infrequent. Gregarious, locally profuse. |
| **Distribution:** | Alps, Apennines, Pyrenees |

# CENTAUREA RHAPONTICA

**Family:** Daisy Family Compositae

**Stem:** 35—110 high, erect, sturdy, thickening towards flower, sulcate, green, downy, foliate

**Leaves:** radical, stalked, large, up to 50 cm long and 12 cm wide, ovate-lanceolate, dentate, grey downy beneath; stalk leaves alternate, somewhat smaller, ovate-lanceolate, lobate, margined, sessile or encircling stalk, reticulate, grey-downy beneath

**Flowers:** terminal, solitary, large, 5—11 cm in diameter, disc florets only, dark pink to purple; spherical involucre, flower bracts rounded, inflated, accumbent, light brown

**Flowering time:** July—September

**Habitat:** 1500—2500 m, predominantly on silicate soils, boulder slopes, scrubby places, wet, stony meadows, windless, warm slopes.
Somewhat rare.
Locally prolific.

**Distribution:** Alps (southern Alps, Julian Alps)

# CENTAUREA JACEA

| | |
|---|---|
| **Family:** | Daisy Family Compositae |
| **Stem:** | 15—60 cm high, erect, hardly branched, slender, foliate, round, rarely angular, hairy, green |
| **Leaves:** | alternate, pinnatifid, oblong to lanceolate, tapering at stalk; upper stem leaves usually undivided, entire, lanceolate, green |
| **Flowers:** | solitary, terminal, 25—50 mm diameter, disc florets only, marginal petals larger, pink to reddish violet; outer bracts brown with scaly, brownish appendages |
| **Flowering time:** | June—September |
| **Habitat:** | up to 1600 m, wet and dry soils, poor grass, meadows, mountain pastures, moorland, edge of paths. Common, widespread, usually prolific. |

**Distribution:** Alps, Pyrenees, Norway

# ALPINE HOUSELEEEK
## Sempervivum alpinum

**Family:** Stonecrop Family Crassulaceae

**Stem:** 10—40 cm high, erect, foliate, glandular hairs

**Leaves:** rosettes up to 8 cm in diameter, leaves fat, fleshy, green with bluish shimmer, ciliate, brownish red prickly tip; erect on the stem, tinged red

**Flowers:** branching pistil, several florets with large corollas, pink to pale red, darker stripes, lanceolate petals, erect stamens, purple style

**Flowering time:** July to September

**Habitat:** 1200—2400 m, basic to acid soils, overgrown detritus, rocky shelves, crevices, steep meadows

**Distribution:** Lechtal Alps

# MOUNTAIN HOUSELEEK

## *Sempervivum montanum*

**Family:** Stonecrop Family Crassulaceae

**Stem:** 5—20 cm high, erect, round, sturdy, green to reddish brown, foliate

**Leaves:** small spherical rosettes, tiny, round, succulent, light green leaves with short red tip, glandular hairs; stem leaves lanceolate, succulent, greenish yellow, red tinged, red tips, accumbent, decurrent, scaly on stem

**Flowers:** one to three terminal, 2—3 cm diameter, 12 to 16 petals, linear to lanceolate, forming a star, purple to violet red, lighter at edge, numerous stamens, ovary and style lemon yellow

**Flowering time:** July—September

**Habitat:** 1800—3200 m, calcifuge, on silicate rock, stony mountain meadows, dwarf shrub heaths, ridges, boulder areas, screes.
Common.

**Distribution:** Alps, Pyrenees, Carpathians

---

**PROTECTED!**

---

# COBWEB HOUSELEEK

## *Sempervivum arachnoideum*

**Family:** Stonecrop Family Crassulaceae

**Stem:** 4—25 cm high, erect, sturdy, green or brownish red, scaly leaved

**Leaves:** ground rosettes, spatulate or ovate, pointed, green, frequently tinged red, cobweb of hairs between the leaves; stem leaves alternate, lanceolate, blunt, fleshy, accumbent, green or brownish red

**Flowers:** usually several in a terminal cyme, corolla approx. 20 mm in diameter, single petals widely lanceolate, pointed, forming a star, red to reddish violet; stamens upright, purple, yellow pollen at top

**Flowering time:** July—September

**Habitat:** 1700—3200 m, calcareous and acid soils, crevices, bouldered slopes, rocks. Somewhat rare.

**Distribution:** Alps, Apennines, Pyrenees

---

| PROTECTED! |
| --- |

# ALPINE BELLS
## Cortusa matthioli

| | |
|---|---|
| **Family:** | Primrose Family Primulaceae |
| **Stem:** | 15—25 cm high, erect or ascending, slender, round, green, leafless |
| **Leaves:** | radical, large, stalked, rounded, lobed, crenate, ribbed, hairy, green |
| **Flowers:** | several flowers, hanging umbel, corolla funnel to bell-shaped, five petals, ovate, dark red to purple, nodding, stalked; sepals slit deeply, green, prominent, hairy |
| **Flowering time:** | July—August |
| **Habitat:** | 1100—1800 m, nutritious soils, damp places, rocks, banks of streams, scrubland, semi-shade. Infrequent. |
| **Distribution:** | Alps |

# AUTUMN CROCUS

## Colchicum autumnale

**Family:** Lily Family Liliaceae

**Stemless!** 6 petals on an elongated tube (mock stem), whitish below, pink tinged above, round, 8—15 cm high

**Leaves:** 3 radical, large, widely lanceolate, fleshy, deep green, shiny, tulip-like, leafless when in flower! Leaves appear in the spring, in the centre 3-merous capsule on sturdy stalk

**Flowers:** solitary, tulip-like, 6 petals forming a funnel-shaped calyx, non-coalescent section 3—7 cm long, elliptic-lanceolate, long, pink to mauve, entire, margined, 3 white styles, 6 golden stamens. Leafless in autumn at flowering time, leaves appear in following spring.

**Flowering time:** August—October

**Habitat:** up to 2200 m, likes nitrogen, clay soil, damp meadows

**Distribution:** Alps, Pyrenees, Apennines

## POISONOUS! COMMON!

# SOLDIER or MILITARY ORCHID

## Orchis militaris

| | |
|---|---|
| **Family:** | Orchid Family Orchidaceae |
| **Stem:** | 20—50 cm high, erect, strong, bare, green, tinged brownish red above, round to slightly angular |
| **Leaves:** | radical, oblong-elliptic, thickish, sheath-like at base, green, shiny, bracts short, pointed, membranous |
| **Flowers:** | dense, pyramid-shaped or oblong spikes, florets stalked, the five upper petals forming a close helmet, pale pink outside, darker stripes inside, outer sepals pointed, inner sepals linear-pointed, somewhat shorter than the outer sepals; lip narrow, three lobes, light red with purple markings; side lobes narrow-linear, central lobe divided into two points with a small tail in between, spur down-curved |
| **Flowering time:** | May—June |
| **Habitat:** | up to 1800 m, calcareous, dry soils, damp marshy ground, meadows with poor soil, clearings, edge of woods and bushes, slopes |

**Distribution:** Alps, Apennines, Pyrenees

| PROTECTED! |
|---|

# EARLY PURPLE ORCHID

## Orchis mascula

| | |
|---|---|
| **Family:** | Orchid Family Orchidaceae |
| **Stem:** | 20—60 cm high, erect, sturdy, round, green-brown, foliate, bare, not branching, usually hollow |
| **Leaves:** | radical, wide-lanceolate, keeled, slightly fleshy, green, unspotted; stem leaves alternate, lanceolate, decurrent, parallel veined, bracts lanceolate, accumbent, violet red |
| **Flowers:** | spikes, single flowers 12—15 mm long, sepals curved, margin wavy, turned up, petals inclined, 3-lobed lip, violet-red or light pink, spur horizontal or up-curved, same length as ovary |
| **Flowering time:** | May—August |
| **Habitat:** | 800—1800 m, calcareous and acid soils, stony meadows, pastures, wetlands, marshy ground, mountain fields. Infrequent. |

**Distribution:** Alps, Apennines, Pyrenees

---

**PROTECTED!**

---

# BLACK VANILLA ORCHID

## *Nigritella nigra*

**Family:** Orchid Family Orchidaceae

**Stem:** 5—20 cm high, erect, round, slightly sulcate, green, slender, foliate

**Leaves:** linear-lanceolate, grooved, pointed, grass-like, green, entire; stem leaves lanceolate, very pointed, sessile or decurrent, green, accumbent

**Flowers:** pyramid-shaped, round, densely flowered heads (shorter than rosy vanilla orchid), single flowers brown to dark wine red, narrow, spreading perianth lobes, lip pointing upwards, tapering at base, spur short, sturdy, pleasantly scented

**Flowering time:** June—August

**Habitat:** 1400—2400 m, warm, sunny mountain meadows, alps, pastures, overgrown ridges.
Infrequent. Gregarious.

**Distribution:** Alps, Apennines, Pyrenees, Norway

# KERNER'S LOUSEWORT
## Pedicularis kerneri

| | |
|---|---|
| **Family:** | Figwort Family Scrophulariaceae |
| **Stem:** | 5—15 cm, curved upwards, slender, green, red tinged, hairy, few leaves, un-branching shoots |
| **Leaves:** | radical, stalked, linear-lanceolate, green, singly pinnate, short teeth, frequently tinged reddish brown or purple, round |
| **Flowers:** | few in loose clusters from top leaf axils, large corolla, approx. 20 mm diameter, five-merous, pink to light purple; upper lip somewhat darker, turning upwards, cut off at top, beak-like, lower lip bare, entire; calyx tubular, brownish red, with small, pointed tips |
| **Flowering time:** | June—September |
| **Habitat:** | 1800—3200 m, lime-deficient, siliceous rock, mountain meadows, overgrown ridges, strips of rock, screes, stony pastures. Infrequent. |
| **Distribution:** | Alps, Pyrenees (central Alps from Salzburg to west Alps) |

# MOSS CAMPION

## Silene acaulis

**Family:** Pink Family Caryophyllaceae

**Stem:** very short, not branching, forming flat cushions, densely crowded, slender stalks, round, green, foliate

**Leaves:** opposite, small, narrow-lanceolate, pointed, numerous, green ciliate

**Flowers:** terminal, solitary, 6—10 mm diameter, five petals, ovate-long, blunt slightly notched, pink to purple, throat whitish with yellow stamens, sometimes forming large, flat cushions

**Flowering times:** June—August

**Habitat:** 1600—3200 m, overgrown, stony soils, grassy ledges of rock, mountain ridges, warm, sunny mountain pastures, boulders.
Quite frequent.

**Distribution:** Alps, Apennines, Pyrenees, Norway

| PROTECTED! |
|:---:|

# MARTAGON LILY

## Lilium martagon

**Family:** Lily Family Liliaceae

**Stem:** 30—100 cm high, erect, sturdy, round, green, foliate

**Leaves:** verticillate, oblong to wide-lanceolate, deep green, parallel veined; upper stem leaves alternate, too, small, lanceolate-pointed, green

**Flowers:** loose cluster, stalked, pendulous, perianth petals long lanceolate, recurved giving turk's cap appearance, pink-purple, brownish red spots; long, curved filaments with ochre-coloured stamens around the style; heavily scented at night

**Flowering time:** July—August

**Habitat:** 1400—2200 m, calcareous soils, mountain meadows, overgrown screes, pastures, edge of woods Infrequent.

**Distribution:** Alps, Pyrenees, Apennines

# ALPINE ROCK—JASMINE

## Androsace alpina

| | |
|---|---|
| **Family:** | Primrose Family Primulaceae |
| **Dwarf bush:** | forming small, loose cushions or flat mats, stalks 2—5 cm high, round, green, foliate |
| **Leaves:** | rosette-like on the stalks, 2—8 cm long, lanceolate to linear, green, densely grouped, starry hairs, pubescent |
| **Flowers:** | on short stalks, corolla 7—9 mm in diameter, five obovate petals, pink to white with yellow throat, single flowers, terminal |
| **Flowering time:** | July—August |
| **Habitat:** | 2200—4200 m, on wet siliceous and shaly rocks, moraines, ridges. Somewhat rare, small amounts locally, completely absent in some areas. |
| **Distribution:** | Alps |

---

### PROTECTED!

---

# MUSK—MALLOW

## Malva moschata

| | |
|---|---|
| **Stem:** | 30—100 cm high, erect, branching, round, green, foliate, sometimes bush-like with many stems, hairy |
| **Leaves:** | few on the stem, alternate, short stalked, palmate, five-merous with narrow, pinnate lobes, dentate, green, hairy, sessile at top |
| **Flowers:** | one to three, terminal or springing from leaf axils of upper stem leaves, large, 4—6 cm in diameter, five petals inversely cordate, straight or notched, pink or white, spreading; numerous prominent stamens, light pink, strong musk scent |
| **Flowering time:** | July—September |
| **Habitat:** | up to 1200 m, nutritious soils, deficient in lime, warm slopes, meadows, pastures, river banks. Somewhat rare, gregarious. |
| **Distribution:** | Alps, southern Scandinavia |

# ALPINE PINK

## Dianthus alpinus

**Family:** Pink Family Caryophyllaceae

**Stem:** 5—15 cm high, erect, slender, round, bare, green, foliate, forming cushions or loose patches

**Leaves:** opposite, lanceolate-linear, 10—20 mm long, 3—5 mm wide, sessile, green, entire, shiny above; rosette leaves linear, blunt, different lengths

**Flowers:** terminal, solitary, large, 20—30 mm in diameter, five petals, inversely cordate, dentate, purple, spreading, pink with darker spots towards the throat; calyx with brownish red scales towards the base, otherwise bare

**Flowering time:** June—August

**Habitat:** 900—2400 m, calcareous and rich soils, warm, stony mountain meadows, overgrown ridges.
Not frequent, completely absent in parts.

**Distribution:** Alps (northern and southern limestone chains of the eastern Alps)

---

### PROTECTED!

---

# CARTHUSIAN PINK

## Dianthus carthusianorum

**Family:** Pink Family Caryophyllaceae

**Stem:** 10—40 cm high, erect, slender, round, green, bare, frequently only one pair of leaves

**Leaves:** radical, long, linear, pointed, slightly carinate, entire, rough, green

**Flowers:** clusters of several heads, flower diameter 12—20 mm, petals obovate, notched, pink to purple, calyx conical-tubular to bell-shaped green to purplish brown, calyx scales dark brown, accumbent

**Flowering time:** June—August

**Habitat:** 800—2800 m, calcareous and neutral soils, meadows, edge of paths, pastures, strips of rock, ridges and overgrown knolls, mountain fields.
Not frequent, gregarious.

**Distribution:** Alps, Apennines, Pyrenees

---

### PROTECTED!

# FLY ORCHID

## Ophrys insectifera

| | |
|---|---|
| **Family:** | Orchid Family Orchidaceae |
| **Stem:** | 15—35 cm high, erect, round, bare, green, foliate |
| **Leaves:** | radical, oblong-ovate, parallel veined, keeled, somewhat fleshy, entire, green; stem leaves oblong-ovate to lanceolate, keeled, light green |
| **Flowers:** | loose raceme with a few florets, florets stalked, nodding, three perigon petals, turned outwards, lanceolate, green, lower lip 10—15 mm long, fly-like with eyes and feelers and fly-like shape, velvety hairs, reddish brown, central bluish zone, deeply lobed, slightly margined |
| **Flowering time:** | April—June |
| **Habitat:** | 800—1700 m, calcareous, poor soils, stony mountain meadows, pastures, often together with lily of the valley. Very rare. |

**Distribution:** Alps

```
PROTECTED!
```

# PAEONY
## Paeonia officinalis

**Family:** Paeony Family Paeoniaceae

**Stem:** 50—90 cm high, erect or ascending, round, strong, green, bare, foliate, not branching

**Leaves:** very large, up to 30 cm long, up to 20 cm wide, trifoliate, deeply cut, multiple pinnate sections, lobes lanceolate or oblong-ovate, pointed, green above, grey green beneath, entire, hairy, stalked

**Flowers:** solitary, terminal, up to 8 cm in diameter, five to eight large petals, bright pink or deep red, wide-ovate to spherical, obtuse, numerous stamens, golden yellow; sepals lanceolate, pointed, spreading, turning out, green or red

**Flowering time:** May—June

**Habitat:** up to 1800 m, on limestone or dolomite rock, stony meadows, warm pastures, by oak bushes, dry slopes, frequently together with broom.
Rare, only found in a few areas.

**Distribution:** Alps, central Apennines (southern Alps, only isolated in the northern Alps)

# VILLOUS PRIMROSE
## Primula hirsuta

| | |
|---|---|
| **Family:** | Primrose Family Primulaceae |
| **Stem:** | 2—7 cm high, erect or pendulous, round, green, foliate, glandular hairs |
| **Leaves:** | ground rosettes, obovate to round, slightly notched, fleshy; glandular hairs |
| **Flowers:** | short stalked, umbel-like clusters, single flowers 12—20 mm in diameter, five petals, inversely cordate, some lobes entire, bright pink, flat spreading, whitish eye; calyx bell-shaped, five-merous, accumbent, green |
| **Flowering time:** | May—June |
| **Habitat:** | 1200—3200 m, siliceous and shaly rocks, ridges, damp valleys. Rare, locally prolific. |
| **Distribution:** | Alps, Pyrenees |

# BIRDSEYE PRIMROSE

## Primula farinosa

| | |
|---|---|
| **Family:** | Primrose Family Primulaceae |
| **Stem:** | 5—25 cm high, erect, round, slender, green, leafless, slightly pubescent |
| **Leaves:** | ground rosettes, oblong, obovate, crenate, green, bare above, mealy white underneath |
| **Flowers:** | several in an umbel, corolla 10—20 mm in diameter, five petals, cordate, two lobes, lilac pink to light purple, yellow eye; calyx short, green, mealy, strongly scented |
| **Flowering time:** | May—August |
| **Habitat:** | 700—2600 m, various soils, wetlands, meadows, poor pastures, rocky strips, marshes. <br> Fairly frequent, gregarious. |
| **Distribution:** | Alps, Pyrenees |

# SPECTACULAR PRIMROSE

## Primula spectabilis

| | |
|---|---|
| **Family:** | Primrose Family Primulaceae |
| **Stem:** | 5—12 cm high, erect, round, bare, green |
| **Leaves:** | radical, oblong-ovate, 6—9 cm long, 2—4 cm wide, bright green, shiny, horny edge, entire |
| **Flowers:** | in a loose umbel, corolla 20—25 mm diameter, five petals, deeply notched, pink, throat whitish or light pink, calyx tube 8—12 mm long, five sepals, narrow-lanceolate, accumbent, green |
| **Flowering time:** | May—August |
| **Habitat:** | 700—2200 m, calcareous soils and those rich in humus, warm, shady pastures, mountain meadows, strips of rock. Rare, large groups locally. |
| **Distribution:** | Alps (meadows and rocky areas around Lake Garda), southern Alps |

---

**PROTECTED!**

---

# ROCK SOAPWORT

## Saponaria ocymoides

| | |
|---|---|
| **Family:** | Pink Family Caryophyllaceae |
| **Stem:** | 10—40 cm long, creeping, pendulous or ascending, cushion-forming, branching, round, reddish brown, hairy, foliate |
| **Leaves:** | obovate, tapering towards leaf stalk, dark green, hairy |
| **Flowers:** | panicles of many flowers, corolla 12—15 mm diameter, petals obovate, entire, pink; tubular calyx, brownish red, glandular hairs, sticky |
| **Flowering time:** | May—September |
| **Habitat:** | 800—2000 m, soils deficient in lime, edge of paths, screes, rocks, warm slopes. Infrequent. |
| **Distribution:** | Alps |

# MEZEREON

## Daphne mezereum

**Family:** Daphne Family Thymelaeaceae

**Stem:** 20—140 cm high, erect shrub, branching, woody, rarely foliate when in flower

**Leaves:** usually near the flower, inversely lanceolate, green, terminal clusters

**Flowers:** clusters of 3 flowers, corolla with 4 petals, calyx short, pink; strong pleasant scent

**Fruits:** bright red berries, some the size of a pea, arranged in spikes at end of branch

**Flowering time:** February—August according to altitude, immediately after snow melts

**Habitat:** up to 2700 m, mixed soils, edge of streams, open woodland, wetlands, hedges, bushes, pastures, boulders

**Distribution:** Alps

# ALPINE SAINFOIN

## Hedysarum hedysaroides

**Family:** Pea Family Leguminosae

**Stem:** 10—30 cm high, erect or ascending, not branching, green

**Leaves:** unevenly pinnate, five to ten pairs of leaves and end leaf, oblong-elliptical, up to 3 cm long, dark above, light green beneath

**Flowers:** one-sided, terminal clusters, up to 40 papilionaceous flowers, purple to reddish violet, arranged like roof tiles, spatulate standard, flowering from bottom to top

**Flowering time:** July—August

**Habitat:** 1600—2800 m, richly calcareous soils, mountain meadows, overgrown screes, rocks, detritus, steep slopes. Infrequent.

**Distribution:** Alps, Pyrenees, Carpathians, Caucasus

**Note:** Alpine sainfoin is frequently confused with mountain sainfoin (Onobrychis montana or saxatilis.) Features of mountain sainfoin: upright petals, pink, darker veins, less flowers on one spike.

# PURPLE SAXIFRAGE
## Saxifraga oppositifolia

**Family:** Saxifrage Family Saxifragaceae

**Stem:** 5—20 mm high, ascending from trailing shoots, round, slender, branching, sometimes cushion-like, green or brown, foliate

**Leaves:** rosettes, very small, ovately pointed, green; stem leaves opposite, narrow-ovate to oval, pointed, grey-green, ciliate, entire

**Flowers:** terminal, solitary, 8—12 mm diameter, five petals, wide-oval or ovate, entire, dark pink to light wine red; calyx bell-shaped, red, sepals small, accumbent, green; stamens purple on brownish stalk, style golden yellow

**Flowering time:** June—August

**Habitat:** 1800—3800 m, calcareous and siliceous rocks, crevices, ridges, moraines, screes.
Rather rare.

**Distribution:** Alps, Apennines, Pyrenees, Norway

---

**PROTECTED!**

---

# CENTAURIUM MINUS

| | |
|---|---|
| **Family:** | Gentian Family Gentianaceae |
| **Stem:** | 10—35 cm high, erect, square, foliate, branching near inflorescence, green |
| **Leaves:** | radical, lanceolate, pointed, small, entire; stem leaves oblong-oval, five veined, sessile, green |
| **Flowers:** | loose cyme, five petals ovate-narrow, spreading, pink, 8—10 mm long, petal tube 8—15 mm long, stamens short, yellow |
| **Flowering time:** | July—September |
| **Habitat:** | up to 1200 m, sunny, warm mountain meadows, pastures, semi-dry turf, open woods. Scattered, entirely absent in places. |

**Distribution:** Alps, Pyrenees

# DEVIL'S CLAW

## Physoplexis comosa

| | |
|---|---|
| **Family:** | Bellflower Family Campanulaceae |
| **Stem:** | 3—15 cm long, usually hanging, round, slender, foliate, green, more rarely erect or ascending |
| **Leaves:** | rosettes, lanceolate to spatulate, coarsely serrate, stalked, green, 4—10 cm long, 1.5—3 cm wide; stem leaves wide-lanceolate, tapering into the stalk, unevenly serrate, green, shiny, 5—10 cm long, 2—3 cm wide |
| **Flowers:** | up to 20 long florets forming a cyme, florets stalked, inflated base, tubular towards the top, conically tapering, long point with curved spur, light pink to light violet; tip dark violet to brownish red, two styles with spirally curved stigmas protruding from the conical spurs |
| **Flowering time:** | July—August (September) |
| **Habitat:** | up to 2700 m, on limestone and dolomite rock, tiny crevices, rocky ledges, boulders. Rare. |

**Distribution:** Alps (southern Alps, Dolomites)

---

**PROTECTED!**

---

# ROSEBAY WILLOWHERB

## Epilobium angustifolium

**Family:** Willowherb Family Onagraceae

**Stem:** 50—150 cm high, erect, round, slender, light green, foliate, not branching

**Leaves:** alternate, sessile, narrow-lanceolate, 6—12 cm long, entire, wavy margin, green, bare

**Flowers:** long, single panicles, corolla 1.5—2.5 cm diameter, four short, spatulate, pink or purplish red petals; stigma four-lobed, stamens yellow, stalked, sepals narrow lanceolate, same colour

**Flowering time:** July—October

**Habitat:** 800—2600 m, calcareous and siliceous rock, screes, stony meadows, clearings, banks of streams, embankments, wetlands, open pine woods.
Frequent, gregarious.

**Distribution:** Alps, Apennines, Pyrenees

Meadow of Alpine flowers, Furgler, Komperdell, Tyrol

# PULSATILLA APIIFOLIA

**Family:**     Buttercup Family Ranunculaceae

**Stem:**       15—40 cm high, upright, sturdy, round,
                green-brown, hairy, foliate

**Leaves:**     radical, stalked, three-merous, pinnate
                sessile up two thirds of stem, hairy

**Flowers:**    terminal, solitary, very large, 50—
                60 mm diameter, usually six petals,
                ovate, pale yellow, delicate violet out-
                side, slightly hairy; numerous stamens,
                pale yellow; fruit: bearded tuft of many
                woolly styles (winged)

**Flowering
time:**         May—July

**Habitat:**    1700—3000 m, mainly siliceous and
                shaly soils, mountain meadows, screes,
                overgrown ridges.
                Rare, prolific locally.

**Distribution:** Alps

---

**PROTECTED!**

---

# ARNICA
## Arnica montana

**Family:**  Daisy Family Compositae

**Stem:**  20—55 cm high, erect, round, green, slightly brownish above, hairy, foliate, frequently branching above

**Leaves:**  ground rosette, usually four leaves, oblong, entire, parallel veined, hairy, light green; stem leaves usually two pairs, opposite, ovate sessile, top leaves lanceolate, pointed, opposite, green

**Flowers:**  terminal heads, sometimes several on short stalks, 5—7 cm diameter, disc florets inside, ray florets outside, long, linear, blunt ends, bright yellow; ovary short, cylindrical, green, hairy, strong scent, flower bracts lanceolate, pointed

**Flowering time:**  June—August

**Habitat:**  800—2500 m, calcareous and marly soils, acid, marshy meadows, heaths, pastures, clearings, high altitude pastures, mountain fields

**Distribution:** Alps, northern Apennines, Pyrenees

# AURICULA or BEARS—EAR

## Primula auricula

| | |
|---|---|
| **Family:** | Primrose Family Primulaceae |
| **Stem:** | 5—25 cm high, erect, round, sturdy, hollow, leafless, green, mealy white |
| **Leaves:** | ground rosette, obovate, entire, green, fleshy, mealy powder |
| **Flowers:** | terminal umbel of many flowers, individual flowers funnel-shaped, corolla spreading, five petals, ovate-roundish, slightly indented, golden yellow, white throat, nodding, mealy, pleasantly scented |
| **Flowering time:** | April—June |
| **Habitat:** | 900—2600 m, calcareous, dolomitic and siliceous soils, rocks, stony mountain meadows, rocky ridges, gorges. Fairly frequent. |
| **Distribution:** | Alps, Apennines |

---

### PROTECTED!

# SPINIEST THISTLE

## Cirsium spinosissimum

**Family:** Daisy Family Compositae

**Stem:** 20—70 cm high, erect or ascending, herbaceous, sometimes branching, frequently several growing from one root

**Leaves:** alternate, sessile, large, sinuate, spiny, toothed, green-yellow, lower leaves grass green; sepals yellow-green, pinnately lobed, sharp spines, toothed, hairy, curling

**Flowers:** several terminal heads, disc florets only, yellowish white, later yellow-brown, surrounded by toothed, spiny, yellowish green bracts, bracts long, pointed, ascending, spreading in sun

**Flowering time:** July—September

**Habitat:** 1500—2800 m, nutritious loamy soils, fine detritus, mountain pastures, screes, snowy valleys

**Distribution:** Alps

# YELLOW GENIPI

## Artemisia mutellina

| | |
|---|---|
| **Family:** | Daisy Family Compositae |
| **Stem:** | 8—25 cm high, erect or ascending, few leaves, silky hairs, slender, reddish brown to greyish green, several from one root |
| **Leaves:** | stalked, digitately lobed, up to five finger-like leaflets, silky hairs, silvery-shiny, stalked, intensive wormwood smell |
| **Flowers:** | spherical heads, upright, panicles or spikes, golden yellow, flower bracts silvery glistening, downy, flowerheads approx. 5—6 mm diameter |
| **Flowering time:** | July—September |
| **Habitat:** | 1700—3600 m, calcareous, shaly and siliceous rocks, crevices, frequently as exposed as edelweiss; not infrequently found together with wood pinks and edelweiss. Rare. |

**Distribution:** Alps, Pyrenees, northern Apennines

---

### ENTIRELY PROTECTED!

---

# GREAT YELLOW GENTIAN
## Gentiana lutea

| | |
|---|---|
| **Family:** | Gentian Family Gentianaceae |
| **Stem:** | 30—130 cm high, upright, strong, round, hollow, green, foliate |
| **Leaves:** | opposite, ovate, wide, pointed, very large, entire, parallel veined, green, considerably smaller towards end of stem |
| **Flowers:** | up to ten in terminal end clusters and at leaf axils, petals long-lanceolate, golden yellow, short stalked |
| **Flowering time:** | July—August |
| **Habitat:** | 1100—2500 m, mainly calcareous soils, mountain meadows, overgrown screes, pastures, slopes |
| **Distribution:** | Alps, Apennines |

---

**PROTECTED!**

---

# SPOTTED GENTIAN

### Gentiana punctata

| | |
|---|---|
| **Family:** | Gentian Family Gentianaceae |
| **Stem:** | 25—60 cm high, erect, round, strong, green-yellow, foliate |
| **Leaves:** | opposite, stalked, ovate-elliptic, pointed, very large, parallel veined, green; upper stem leaves more lanceolate, sessile |
| **Flowers:** | terminal and in clusters at upper leaf axils, erect; flowers large, bell-shaped, five to seven petals, pointed, dullish pale yellow, grey-brown spotted; sepals accumbent, bell-shaped, green |
| **Flowering time:** | July—September |
| **Habitat:** | 1500—2800 m, calcareous and siliceous soils, mountain meadows, pastures, stony places, alpine turf. Quite frequent. |

**Distribution:** Alps

---

**PROTECTED!**

# LAMARCK'S WOLFSBANE

## *Aconitum lamarckii*

**Family:**      Buttercup Family Ranunculaceae

**Stem:**      50—140 cm high, erect, round, some-times angular, slender, green, hairy, foliate, usually several from one root

**Leaves:**      radical, long-stalked, palmate, deeply cut, some pinnate, green, hairy; stem leaves sessile, palmate, five to seven segments with rhomboid sections, smaller towards end of stem

**Flowers:**      loose racemes or on little branches, florets stalked, conspicuously high helmet, 25—40 mm long, slender, nodding, pale cloudy yellow

**Flowering time:**      July—August

**Habitat:**      1400—2400 m, calcareous, stony soils, screes, avalanche lines, mountain fields, boulders, overgrown ridges, edge of woods, clearings.
Quite frequent, prolific in parts.

**Distribution:** Alps, Apennines, Pyrenees, Jura

---

### PROTECTED! POISONOUS!

---

# GIANT CATSEAR

## Hypochoeris uniflora

**Family:**  Daisy Family Compositae

**Stem:**  10—50 cm high, erect, round, very strong, thickening towards the flower-head, green; stiff hairs

**Flowers:**  terminal, single heads, 30—50 mm diameter, ray florets long, linear, straight or slightly toothed, golden yellow; calyx in a head, small flower bracts, dark green, stiff hairs, bright, conspicuous plant

**Flowering time:**  July—August

**Habitat:**  1400—2500 m, poor, warm soils, mountain meadows, pastures, heathery moors, Alpine rose sites. Scattered.

**Distribution:** Alps, Carpathians

# LARGE YELLOW FOXGLOVE

## Digitalis grandiflora

| | |
|---|---|
| **Family:** | Figwort Family Scrophulariaceae |
| **Stem:** | 25—100 cm high, erect, very strong, round, green, foliate, hairy |
| **Leaves:** | alternate, wide-lanceolate, sessile, slightly toothed, pronounced venation, green; fluffy hairs beneath |
| **Flowers:** | in a dense spike on one side, tubular bells, 30—40 mm long, short stalks, five points, lower lip three-lobed, lemon yellow, dotted brown inside, calyx slightly flattened, edge of corolla turning back, hairy, nodding |
| **Flowering time:** | July—September |
| **Habitat:** | 1100—1800 m, calcareous and siliceous rock, warm mountain meadows, edge of fir woods, sunny slopes, clearings, boulders. Not frequent, locally prolific. |
| **Distribution:** | Alps, Pyrenees |

---

**PROTECTED!**

---

# POTENTILLA RECTA

| | |
|---|---|
| **Family:** | Rose Family Rosaceae |
| **Stem:** | 20—60 cm high, erect, several from one root, branching above, round, green-brown, hairy, foliate |
| **Leaves:** | radical leaves long-stalked, five to seven, serrate, green, hairy; stem leaves alternate, usually seven-merous, deeply serrate; bristly hairs |
| **Flowers:** | on long stalks, terminal, approx. 2—3 cm in diameter, five petals, heart-shaped, pale yellow, short stamens in centre somewhat darker yellow, inflorescence on main stem in loose panicle with many buds, flower only spreading in warm, sunny weather |
| **Flowering time:** | June—July |
| **Habitat:** | up to 1200 m, edge of paths, poor turf, dry, warm slopes, gravel pits, edge of bushes and woods. Gregarious, scattered to rare. |
| **Distribution:** | Alps, Apennines, Pyrenees |

# LADY'S SLIPPER ORCHID

## Cypripedium calceolus

**Family:** Orchid Family Orchidaceae

**Stem:** 20—60 cm high, erect, strong, round, bare, green, foliate

**Leaves:** stem leaves, large, widely lanceolate, strong, parallel veined, entire, some margined, encircling stalk and decurrent, deep green, topmost leaves smaller, pointed and usually ribbed lengthways

**Flowers:** on short, curved stalks emerging at stipule, usually one to three flowers turning to one side; four pointed, twisted, purplish brown petals, very large lip, resembling a clog, 3—5 cm long, hollow, golden yellow, lightly veined in brown, purple spotted nectary at base of lip

**Flowering time:** May—July

**Habitat:** 900—1500 m, calcareous, loamy soils, semi-shaded; edge of bushes and woods, open coniferous forests, gorges, banks of streams, slopes, pines

**Distribution:** Alps, Pyrenees, Norway

**Note:** the loveliest and most precious local orchid!

| PROTECTED! |
| :---: |

# LARGE FLOWERED LEOPARDSBANE

## Doronicum grandiflorum

| | |
|---|---|
| **Family:** | Daisy Family Compositae |
| **Stem:** | 20—60 cm high, erect, round, hollow, green, glandular, hairy, foliate |
| **Leaves:** | radical, stalked, large, widely lanceolate, sinuately toothed, green, hairy; stem leaves sometimes sessile or stalked, serrate |
| **Flowers:** | terminal, soliatary, very large (3—6 cm diameter) ray florets, linear, golden yellow; disc florets clustered in centre, golden yellow; sepals lanceolate, green, hairy |
| **Flowering time:** | July—September |
| **Habitat:** | 1700—2800 m, loamy, poor soils, screes, pastures, edge of streams, bouldery slopes.<br>Quite frequent. |

**Distribution:** Alps

# YELLOW BELLFLOWER

## Campanula thyrsoidea

| | |
|---|---|
| **Family:** | Bellflower Family Campanulaceae |
| **Stem:** | 10—50 cm high, erect, very strong, round, green-brown, foliate, bristly hairs |
| **Leaves:** | alternate, sessile, oblong linear, entire, wavy, green with lighter central vein, hairy; upper leaves narrower, linear, somewhat longer than the flowers, pointed |
| **Flowers:** | dense cylindrical spike, cup to bell-shaped flowers, 20—40 mm long, pale yellow, slightly upright, long pistil and few stamens, green-yellow |
| **Flowering time:** | June—August |
| **Habitat:** | 1500—2500 m, calcareous and siliceous soils, sunny mountain meadows, warm slopes. Not frequent. Few areas in which it is prolific. |

**Distribution:** Alps

# WHITISH HAWKWEED

## Hieracium intybaceum All.

**Family:** Daisy Family Compositae

**Stem:** 8—20 cm high, erect, one or more heads, glandular hairs, green, thickening towards flowerhead, foliate

**Leaves:** rosettes, long-lanceolate, coarsely serrate, slightly folded downwards, sticky glandular hairs, green, bracts linear, opposite, glandular

**Flowers:** terminal, large flowerheads, 3—5 cm diameter, yellowish white, ray florets blunt toothed at end

**Flowering time:** July—August

**Habitat:** 1800—2700 m, stony soils, overgrown pastures, meadows, rocky detritus, rocky regions.
Not frequent, scattered.

**Distribution:** Alps (western Alps, southern Alps, northern limestone Alps)

**Note:** Hieracium intybaceum has beautifully bright flowers in Alpine terrain, involucre of ray florets little contrast. Alpine plant, rarely subalpine.

# WULFEN'S HOUSELEEK

## Sempervivum wulfenii

**Family:** Stonecrop Family Crassulaceae

**Stem:** 10—25 cm high, erect or ascending in an arc, round, strong, scaly, foliate, yellow-green

**Leaves:** large rosettes, ovate-pointed, succulent, with glandular hairs, green, tips tinged red; stem leaves alternate, lanceolately pointed, sessile, decurrent, yellow to green, accumbent

**Flowers:** heads at the end of the stem, flower consisting of 10—18 petals, linear-pointed, spreading in a star, golden yellow, with glandular hairs; numerous stamens, purple, style yellow to green

**Flowering time:** July—September

**Habitat:** 1700—2600 m, calcifuge, siliceous rock, sunny meadows, boulders, rocky ridges.
Not frequent, prolific locally.

**Distribution:** Alps (predominantly main Alpine ridge)

---

**PROTECTED!**

---

# ALPINE POPPY

## Papaver alpinum

| | |
|---|---|
| **Family:** | Poppy Family Papaveraceae |
| **Stem:** | 5—25 cm high, erect or ascending in a curve, slender, round, dark green, bristly hairs, several from one root |
| **Leaves:** | radical, rosettes, clustered, oblong-oval, singly to doubly pinnate, grey-green, hairy |
| **Flowers:** | terminal, solitary, erect, 40—60 mm diameter, five petals, obovate-round, some obtuse, golden yellow, pistil and numerous stamens also golden yellow; sepals shaped like a semi-basin, green, hairy outside |
| **Flowering time:** | July—August |
| **Habitat:** | 2000—2700 m, calcareous and dolomite rock, screes, detritus, moraines. Rather rare. |

**Distribution:** Alps, Apennines, Pyrenees

---

## PROTECTED!

---

# CARNIOLAN GROUNDSEL

## Senecio carniolicus

**Family:** Daisy Family Compositae

**Stem:** 5—20 cm high, towering, grey downy, sparsely foliate, green with grey shimmer

**Leaves:** radical, rosettes, obovate, crenate to pinnately lobed, downy, seldom bare, green with grey shimmer, stem leaves spatulate, pinnately lobed with narrow lobes, green — grey downy, stalked

**Flowers:** terminal umbels or clusters, several flowerheads, golden yellow, up to 1.5 cm large, flower bracts only slightly crenate, green-grey

**Flowering time:** July—October

**Habitat:** 1700—3200 m, soils deficient in lime, siliceous rock, recesses in the rock, moraines, screes, mountain ridges. Quite frequent.

**Distribution:** eastern Alps

# SHRUBBY MILKWORT

## Polygala chamaebuxus

| | |
|---|---|
| **Family:** | Milkwort Family Polygalaceae |
| **Stem:** | 5—25 cm long, prostrate, creeping or ascending, branching, runners, round, strong, green-brown, some woody, foliate (small subshrub) |
| **Leaves:** | alternate, sessile, ovate, blunt, tapering into stalk, entire, shiny above, leathery, evergreen |
| **Flowers:** | terminal, clustered or emerging from upper leaf axils, whitish yellow erect wings; keel four-lobed, bright yellow or purple |
| **Flowering time:** | February—August (some as from November) |
| **Habitat:** | 600—2500 m, calcareous, poor soils, rocks, meadows, pastures, dry turf, open fir woods, amongst Alpine roses and pines. Frequent, gregarious. |
| **Distribution:** | Alps, Apennines, Pyrenees, Jura, Carpathians |

123

# ALPINE AVENS

## Geum montanum

**Family:** Rose Family Rosaceae

**Stem:** 5—30 cm high, erect, strong, round, green-brown, foliate, hairy, no runners

**Leaves:** radical, rosettes, very large, oblong-spatulate, pinnate, reniform, lobed end leaf, lobes deeply notched, green, hairy, stalked; stem leaflets three or five-lobed, wide-lanceolate, hairy, alternate, sessile

**Flowers:** terminal, solitary, 25—50 mm diameter, five to six petals, ovate-round, some margined, golden yellow; stamens and style somewhat darker yellow; fruit a tuft of twisted, hairy styles, brown-red, serving as wings for the seeds. Calyx with several points, lanceolate, green, accumbent, hairy

**Flowering time:** July—August

**Habitat:** 1700—3200 m, siliceous and shaly soils, sunny mountain meadows, strips of rock, by Alpine roses, stony slopes, boulders.
Scattered.

**Distribution:** Alps, Apennines, Pyrenees

# CREEPING AVENS

## Geum reptans

| | |
|---|---|
| **Family:** | Rose Family Rosaceae |
| **Stem:** | 5—20 cm high, prostrate or ascending, foliate, reddish brown like the long runners, hairy |
| **Leaves:** | rosettes, pinnate, leaflet notched, dark green, shiny, hairy beneath, stalked |
| **Flowers:** | terminal, usually seven petals, obovate, golden yellow, slightly notched, entire; numerous stamens, sometimes a darker yellow, five sepals, pointed, brown-green, hairy; fruit bright red-brown, fluffily curling tufts act as wings for the seeds |
| **Flowering time:** | July—August |
| **Habitat:** | 1800—3200 m, soils deficient in lime, rocky ridges, screes, moraines, boulders.<br>Rather rare. |
| **Distribution:** | Alps |

# COWSLIP
### Primula veris

| | |
|---|---|
| **Family:** | Primrose Family Primulaceae |
| **Stem:** | 8—35 cm high, erect, strong, round, yellow-green, slightly hairy, leafless |
| **Leaves:** | radical, rosettes, oblong ovate, with wide, flat stalk, notched, crinkled, mignonette green, hairy young leaves turned back |
| **Flowers:** | terminal, one-sided umbel, corolla funnel-shaped, five petals, inversely cordate, notched, golden yellow, orange throat, spotted; calyx long, inflated, green, stalked, hairy |
| **Flowering time:** | March—May |
| **Habitat:** | 800—2200 m, sunny, warm soils, mountain meadows, pastures, open deciduous and mixed woodland, sunny slopes, stony hillsides. Infrequent, gregarious. |

**Distribution:** Alps, Apennines, Pyrenees

# YELLOW OX—EYE

## Bupthalmum salicifolium

| | |
|---|---|
| **Family:** | Daisy Family Compositae |
| **Stem:** | 20—60 cm high, erect or ascending, branching, green, round, foliate, bush-shaped plant |
| **Leaves:** | radical, stalked, cordate to wide lance-olate, serrate-crenate, green; stem leaves lanceolate, sessile, some encircling stalk, toothed, ciliate |
| **Flowers:** | terminal on the shoots, corolla 4—6 cm in diameter, outside ray florets, linear, blunt, toothed, golden yellow; inside disc florets, glandular, golden yellow; sepals very small, lanceolate, green, accumbent |
| **Flowering time:** | July—September |
| **Habitat:** | 800—2000 m, soils rich in humus, stony turf, mountain meadows, banks of streams, warm slopes, ridges of rock. Quite frequent. |
| **Distribution:** | Alps, northern Apennines |

# MOSSY SAXIFRAGE

## Saxifraga bryoides

**Family:** Saxifrage Family Saxifragaceae
Cushion plant, moss-like, dense, green, little stems up to 6 cm high, round, slender, brownish red

**Leaves:** basal leaves linear-lanceolate, pointed, ciliate at edge, moss-like, rosettes, green, very small, stem leaves small, accumbent, inconspicuous, green-brown

**Flowers:** terminal, single flowers, five petals 4—6 mm long, elliptical-pointed, star-shaped, cream coloured, darker beige on ground, ten stamens, protruding, calyx in spiny points

**Flowering time:** July—August

**Habitat:** 1900—4000 m, siliceous and shaly detritus, glacial moraines, crevices, screes

**Distribution:** Alps, Pyrenees, Carpathians, Balkans

**Note:** Saxifraga bryoides is one of the Alpine flowering plants found at the highest altitudes (up to 4200 m)

---

### ENTIRELY PROTECTED!

---

# HEARTSEASE
## Viola tricolor

**Family:**  Violet Family Violaceae

**Stem:**  8—20 cm long, prostrate or ascending, branching, angular, foliate, slender, hairy, green

**Flowers:**  terminal, solitary, large, 2.5—5 cm in diameter, five petals, spreading, obovate, yellowish white — light violet (tricoloured), marked with dark red lines towards base, spur short, blunt; five sepals, lanceolate, 20—30 mm long, green, accumbent

**Leaves:**  alternate, ovate-lanceolate, long, pointed, green; stipules lanceolate, pinnate, green

**Flowering time:**  June—August (September)

**Habitat:**  up to 2400 m, calcareous, poor soils, edges of fields, embankments, walls, fine detritus, cornfields, potato fields, screes.
Scattered, gregarious.

**Distribution:** Alps, Apennines, Pyrenees, Norway

# GLOBEFLOWER

## Trollius europaeus

| | |
|---|---|
| **Family:** | Buttercup Family Ranunculaceae |
| **Stem:** | 10—70 cm high, erect, slender, round, sometimes branching, green, bare, foliate |
| **Leaves:** | radical, long stalked, palmate, deeply cut, crenate-serrate, green, slightly hairy; stem leaves sessile, five or three merous, lobes lanceolate, serrate, green |
| **Flowers:** | terminal, spherical head, 20—40 mm diameter, up to fifteen almost round petals in a depressed globe, golden yellow, narrow stamens and nectary inside |
| **Flowering time:** | June—July |
| **Habitat:** | 700—2400 m, damp meadows, grassy ridges, mountain pastures, banks of streams. Quite frequent. |

**Distribution:** Alps, Apennines, Pyrenees, Norway

Field of flowers near Namlos, Lechtal Alps, Tyrol

# ALPINE COLUMBINE

## Aquilegia alpina

| | |
|---|---|
| **Family:** | Buttercup Family Ranunculaceae |
| **Stem:** | 20—65 cm high, ramose, round, strong, green, red tinged, bare, foliate |
| **Leaves:** | radical leaves stalked, double trifoliate, crenate, deeply cut, dark green; stem leaves sessile, secondary leaflets trifoliae, narrow-lanceolate, sessile |
| **Flowers:** | long-stalked, nodding, large, 4—8 cm in diameter, five sepals, ovate, pointed, five long spurs hooked at end, five ovate petals — round, bright blue, bracts projecting, golden yellow stamens, protruding |
| **Flowering time:** | July—August |
| **Habitat:** | 1200—2500 m, loose soils, meadows, open woods, edge of woods, clearings, bushes, wetlands, pastures. Not frequent. |

**Distribution:** Alps, northern Apennines

---

### PROTECTED!

# ALPINE ASTER

## Aster alpinus

| | |
|---|---|
| **Family:** | Daisy Family Compositae |
| **Stem:** | 10—25 cm high, erect, foliate, green, round, pubescent |
| **Leaves:** | radical, stalked, spatulate, green, central vein, stem leaflets lanceolate, sessile, green |
| **Flowers:** | terminal, single head, one row of ray florets, linear, violet to pink; disc florets yellow; bracts green, several rows, accumbent |
| **Flowering time:** | June—August |
| **Habitat:** | 1000—2600 m, dry, sunny soils, stony, overgrown slopes, rocky ridges, pastures, crevices. Quite frequent. |
| **Distribution:** | Alps, Pyrenees, Apennines |

# TRUMPET GENTIAN
## Gentiana kochiana

| | |
|---|---|
| **Family:** | Gentian Family Gentianaceae |
| **Stem:** | 2—5 cm long, erect or prostrate, green-brownish, strong, foliate |
| **Leaves:** | radical, rosettes, wide-elliptic, herbaceous, blunt, soft, shiny, grass green; ovate stem leaflets in one or two pairs |
| **Flowers:** | terminal, solitary, large, 5—7 cm long, flowers in trumpets, five points, spreading, bright white, tinged a delicate olive green outside, olive green spotting inside, white connecting membrane in the wide indentations between the petals, 5 stamens, whitish style and stigma, sepal teeth projecting |
| **Flowering time:** | May—August |
| **Habitat:** | 1400—2800 m, grassy slopes, screes, mountain meadows, pastures. Quite frequent. |
| **Distribution:** | Alps, Pyrenees, Apennines, Apuan Alps |

## PROTECTED!

# SPRING GENTIAN
## Gentiana verna

| | |
|---|---|
| **Family:** | Gentian Family Gentianaceae |
| **Stem:** | 3—8 cm high, erect, round, green, foliate |
| **Leaves:** | radical, rosettes, elliptic-lanceolate, entire, green, different lengths; stem leaflets opposite, small-lanceolate, decurrent |
| **Flowers:** | terminal, solitary, corolla spread out flat, approx. 25 mm diameter, five petal lobes, wide lanceolate or ovate, azure, throat whitish, ciliate; calyx tubular, green-blue outside; sepals lanceolate, long, pointed, green |
| **Flowering time:** | March—July |
| **Habitat:** | 800—3000 m, calcareous and siliceous rock, meadows, sunny pastures, boulders, alps, rocky ledges. Quite frequent. |
| **Distribution:** | Alps, Pyrenees, Abruzzi |

# BLADDER GENTIAN

## Gentiana ultriculosa

**Family:** Gentian Family Gentianaceae

**Stem:** 12—25 cm high, erect, angular, branching, green-brown, foliate, bare

**Leaves:** rosettes, obovate, blunt, green; stem leaflets in pairs, long-lanceolate, sessile, green

**Flowers:** one-sided, stalked, 5 lobes, spreading, 15—25 mm diameter, azure blue, tube whitish inside; calyx very long, narrow, broad wings, stalk emerging from pair of opposite leaves

**Flowering time:** May—August

**Habitat:** 800—2200 m, stony, sandy soils, pastures, meadows, wetlands, screes, bogs.
Not frequent, rare in places.

**Distribution:** Alps

# COMMON MONKSHOOD

### Aconitum napellus

| | |
|---|---|
| **Family:** | Buttercup Family Ranunculaceae |
| **Stem:** | 40—140 cm high, erect, strong, round to angular, green to brown, foliate, hollow |
| **Leaves:** | alternate, palmate, cut to the middle in five to seven sections, crenate, green, lower leaves stalked, upper leaves sessile |
| **Flowers:** | long spike-like raceme, five petals, top one helmet-like, deep blue, two stalked nectaries and numerous white stamens protruding from corolla |
| **Flowering time:** | July—September |
| **Habitat:** | 900—2700 m, nutritious soils, alpine pastures, crevices, overgrown ridges. Quite frequent. |
| **Distribution:** | Alps, Pyrenees |
| **Note:** | entire plant extremely poisonous. |

---

**PROTECTED!**

---

# DOLOMITES BELLFLOWER

## Campanula morettiana

**Family:** Bellflower Family Campanulaceae

**Stem:** 1—6 cm long, hanging or ascending, round, green, stiff hairs, foliate, several from one root

**Leaves:** wide-oval to round, toothed, green, stiff hairs, lower leaves stalked, upper leaves sessile

**Flowers:** terminal, solitary, 1.5—2.5 cm diameter, funnel-shaped — bell-shaped, five petals, blue violet to red violet, hairy; calyx accumbent, very small, green, five sepals; stamens yellow

**Flowering time:** August—October

**Habitat:** 1500—2400 m, calcareous and dolomite rock, in the finest cracks and crevices, in more exposed places than edelweiss and wormwood.
Rare.

**Distribution:** Alps (Dolomites from the South Tyrol to Venetia)

| PROTECTED! |
| --- |

# MOUNT CENIS BELLFLOWER

## Campanula cenisia

**Family:** Bellflower Family Campanulaceae

**Stem:** 3—25 cm long, sprawling, prostrate, round, slender, bare, green, foliate

**Leaves:** rosettes, ovate — round, entire, fleshy, green, ciliate; stem leaves wide-lanceolate, opposite, sessile, smaller, green, shiny

**Flowers:** on short stalks, terminal, solitary, bells, angular, corolla five-lobed, deeply cut, steel blue to slate grey, spreading, corolla diameter 15—25 mm, pistil and stamens yellow, calyx with five sepals, lanceolate, green, rough hairs, accumbent

**Flowering time:** July—September

**Habitat:** 2000—2900 m, shaly and calcareous rocks, screes, detritus, ridges. Very rare.

**Distribution:** Alps (western Alps) eastwards as far as the Lechtaler Alps

# CREEPING BELLFLOWER
## Campanula rapunculoides

| | |
|---|---|
| **Family:** | Bellflower Family Campanulaceae |
| **Stem:** | 15—80 cm high, erect, slender, round, green-brown, foliate, slightly hairy |
| **Leaves:** | alternate, sessile, ovate-lanceolate-oblong, dark green, crenate, reticulate, upper stem leaflets narrow, pointed, lower ones long-stalked, ovate-triangular |
| **Flowers:** | one-sided spike, numerous flowers, short stalked, funnel-shaped-campanulate, five petals curved backwards, nodding, up to 3.5 cm long and 3 cm diameter, light violet to dark blue-mauve, less frequently white, ciliate, five stamens, whitish |
| **Flowering time:** | June—September |
| **Habitat:** | 600—1700 m, various soils, stony meadows, pastures, banks. Scattered, gregarious, prolific locally. |

**Distribution:** Alps, Apennines

# BEARDED BELLFLOWER

## Campanula barbata

| | |
|---|---|
| **Family:** | Bellflower Family Campanulaceae |
| **Stem:** | 10—35 cm high, erect, strong, round, foliate, hairy |
| **Leaves:** | radical, oblong-spatulate, entire, green, hairy; stem leaves smaller, lanceolate, green, sessile, entire, hairy on both sides |
| **Flowers:** | one-sided raceme, nodding, stalked, ventricose-campanulate, five points, pale blue to mauve, some white, five epicalyx sepals, hairy, five calyx sepals, accumbent, pointed, green |
| **Flowering time:** | June—August |
| **Habitat:** | 1500—2500 m, poor soils, deficient in lime, mountain meadows, pastures, often gregarious with arnica. Frequent. |
| **Distribution:** | Alps, Norway |

# CLUSTERED BELLFLOWER

## Campanula glomerata

| | |
|---|---|
| **Family:** | Bellflower Family Campanulaceae |
| **Stem:** | 25—50 cm high, erect, strong, angular, foliate, slightly hairy, green, brown tinged |
| **Leaves:** | radical, stalked, cordate, slightly serrate; stem leaves oblong to lanceolate, alternate, sessile, crenate-serrate; bracts smaller, just beneath flower cluster, green, irregularly serrate |
| **Flowers:** | terminal, clustered, some in upper leaf axils, corolla funnel to bell-shaped, five petals, blue-violet, 1.5—2.5 cm diameter, 1.5—3 cm long, erect, five stamens, white |
| **Flowering time:** | June—August |
| **Habitat:** | 800—1700 m, poor soils, mountain meadows, overgrown stony ground and slopes, pastures. Scattered. |
| **Distribution:** | Alps, Jura |

# PEACH—LEAVED BELLFLOWER

### Campanula persicifolia

| | |
|---|---|
| **Family:** | Bellflower Family Campanulaceae |
| **Stem:** | 30—100 cm high, erect, round, slender, green, sometimes reddish brown above, foliate, bare |
| **Leaves:** | lower leaves oblong-ovate, tapering to stem, entire, upper stem leaves sessile, lanceolate to linear, light green, margin slightly serrate |
| **Flowers:** | loose racemes, short stalks, broad bells, 2.5—4 cm diameter, five petals, wide-ovate, pointed, light violet to light blue, nodding, edge turned back; stigma three-merous, whitish yellow, five dark yellow stamens, five-merous calyx, lobes short, green, accumbent |
| **Flowering time:** | May—August |
| **Habitat:** | up to 2000 m, poor soils, sunny meadows, open woods, bushes, edge of woods, mountain fields, warm slopes, clearings. Scattered, gregarious, locally prolific. |

**Distribution:** Alps

# SCHEUCHZER'S HAREBELL

## Campanula scheuchzeri

| | |
|---|---|
| **Family:** | Bellflower Family Campanulaceae |
| **Stem:** | 8—30 cm high, erect or ascending, sometimes crooked, slender, green, foliate, slightly hairy |
| **Leaves:** | radical leaves rounded, long-stalked, notched, dark green; stem leaves alternate, oblong-linear, upper leaves narrowly lanceolate, acicular, entire |
| **Flowers:** | mainly solitary, terminal, erect, bell-shaped, 20—25 mm diameter, 20—35 mm long, corolla with five petals, slightly turned back, blue-violet; sepals narrow-acicular, turning out, green; five stamens, yellow to white |
| **Flowering time:** | July—September |
| **Habitat:** | 800—3000 m, nutritious soils deficient in lime, mountain meadows, pastures, rocky strips, overgrown ridges, stony slopes, edge of woods, overgrown screes. Scattered, gregarious. |

**Distribution:** Alps, Pyrenees

# NETTLE-LEAVED BELLFLOWER

## Campanula trachelium

| | |
|---|---|
| **Family:** | Bellflower Family Campanulaceae |
| **Stem:** | 25—90 cm high, erect, strong, angular, reddish brown, hairy, branching, foliate |
| **Leaves:** | alternate, wide-lanceolate, toothed, green, hairy, lower leaves stalked, nettle-like |
| **Flowers:** | loose, one-sided raceme, flowers large, 3—5 cm long, 2—3 cm diameter, bells, corolla with five petals, light blue-violet, more rarely white, margin ciliate, style thin, stigma three-merous, whitish |
| **Flowering time:** | July—August |
| **Habitat:** | 900—2000 m, stony, loose loamy soils, sunny or semi-shaded meadows, edge of woods, pastures. Rather rare, gregarious. |
| **Distribution:** | Alps, Pyrenees |

# KING OF THE ALPS
### Eritrichium nanum

**Family:** Borage Family Boraginaceae

**Stem:** up to 4 cm high, erect, round, slender, foliate, green; forming cushions or loose turf

**Leaves:** in rosettes, lanceolate-spatulate, 6—12 mm long, 2—5 mm wide, green-grey, rough hairs, sessile; numerous rosettes forming small cushions

**Flowers:** solitary, more rarely several on one stalk, terminal, very small, 4—8 mm in diameter, petals obovate to round, flat spreading, sky blue, yellow throat; calyx very small, five-merous, florets with bracts, green

**Flowering time:** July—September

**Habitat:** 2500—3400 m, on dolomite and siliceous rock, fine screes, snowy valleys, crevices, ridges, moraines, near glaciers and defying extremes of weather. Rare.

**Distribution:** Alps, Carpathians, Caucasus (central Alps and Dolomites).

---
**PROTECTED!**
---

# COMMON PASQUE FLOWER
## Pulsatilla vulgaris

**Family:** Buttercup Family Ranunculaceae

**Stem:** 6—35 cm high, erect, strong, green-grey, hairy, foliate

**Leaves:** radical leaves rosette-like, long stalked, 2-pinnate and 3-pinnate, narrow-linear tips, pointed, green, hairy, appearing after flowering; top leaves whorled, approx. half-way up stem, pointing outwards, fluffy hairs

**Flowers:** solitary, large, 6 sepals, 3—4 cm long, oblong-ovate, light violet, hairy outside, bell-shaped, tips turned back, numerous ovaries with long violet stigmas surrounded by numerous golden stamens

**Flowering time:** March—May

**Habitat:** 800—1700 m, calcareous, stony soils, meadows, stony slopes.
Rather rare.

**Distribution:** Alps, Jura, Pyrenees, Apennines

---

### COMPLETELY PROTECTED! POISONOUS!

---

# ALPINE ERYNGO or QUEEN OF THE ALPS

### Eryngium alpinum

**Family:** Carrot Family Umbelliferae

**Stem:** 40—100 cm high, erect, one to several heads, bare, sulcate, green to light brown, foliate

**Leaves:** stem leaves at top three-lobed to palmately lobed, sessile, bluish, basal leaves oval-triangular, dentate-serrate, stalked

**Flowers:** umbel of many amethyst blue florets surrounded by light blue tinged, spiny bracts which open in the sun

**Flowering time:** July—September

**Habitat:** 1200—2400 m, calcareous soils, stony pastures, meadows, by dwarf pines, nutritious land, sheltered from wind, slopes.

**Distribution:** Alps, predominantly western Alps

---

### COMPLETELY PROTECTED!

# STICKY PRIMROSE
## *Primula glutinosa*

| | |
|---|---|
| **Family:** | Primrose Family Primulaceae |
| **Stem:** | 2—8 cm high, erect, slender, round, greenish brown, glandular, leafless |
| **Leaves:** | radical, lanceolate-cuneate, rather fleshy, toothed, green |
| **Flowers:** | one to seven in an umbel, five petals, 10—15 mm diameter, petal lobes deeply notched, violet — violet pink, throat whitish, glandular hairs with darker eye, fragrant. Calyx accumbent, brown to dark red, scaly |
| **Flowering time:** | July—August |
| **Habitat:** | 1800—3000 m, neutral to acid soils, siliceous rock, overgrown ridges, stony pastures, snowy valleys, screes. Frequent, scattered, prolific locally. |

**Distribution:** Alps (central Alps)

### PROTECTED!

# ALPINE SNOWBELL

## *Soldanella alpina*

**Family:** Primrose Family Primulaceae

**Stem:** 5—15 cm high, erect or ascending in a curve, round, slender, brown-red, bare, leafless, curved at top

**Leaves:** radical, stalked, reniform-round, small, entire, green, matt-shiny, cut at base, matt green beneath

**Flowers:** one to three on stem, funnel to bell-shaped, deeply fringed, blue-violet, more rarely white, nodding; five sepals, lanceolate, turned outwards, green-brown, pistil protruding, long-pointed

**Flowering time:** April—August (depending on when snow melts)

**Habitat:** 1200—2800 m, calcareous, damp soils, loamy pastures, mountain meadows, snowy valleys.
Quite frequent, prolific locally.

**Distribution:** Alps, Apennines, Pyrenees

# DWARF SNOWBELL

## Soldanella pusilla

**Family:** Primrose Family Primulaceae

**Stem:** 3—10 cm high, erect, round, slender, reddish brown, leafless, nodding

**Leaves:** basal rosettes, short-stalked, reniform, round, entire, green, prominent ribs, shiny, smaller than in Alpine Snowbell

**Flowers:** solitary, nodding, tubular bells, 9—16 mm long, shallow fringe, violet to pink, dark red stripes inside; five sepals, lanceolate, accumbent, violet

**Flowering time:** May—August

**Habitat:** 1500—3000 m, damp soils deficient in lime, overgrown ridges, mountain meadows, snowy valleys, pastures. Infrequent.

**Distribution:** Alps, north-west Apennines

# ALPINE PANSY

## Viola alpina

| | |
|---|---|
| **Family:** | Violet Family Violaceae |
| **Stem:** | 2—4 cm high, erect or ascending, round, slender, green, several from one branching root |
| **Leaves:** | radical, rosettes, small, ovate, notched, green; stipules growing into leaf stalk |
| **Flowers:** | terminal, solitary, conspicuously large, 30—40 mm diameter, petals spreading, obovate, deep violet, darker veins, throat light yellow, spur slightly up-turned |
| **Flowering time:** | June—October |
| **Habitat:** | 1500—2400 m, calcareous soils, stony meadows, banks of streams, pastures, ridges, screes, boulders. Not frequent, gregarious. |
| **Distribution:** | Alps, Carpathians (northern limestone Alps, more rarely central Alps) |

181

# ROUND-HEADED RAMPION

## Phyteuma orbiculare

**Family:** Bellflower Family Campanulaceae

**Stem:** 15—50 cm high, erect or ascending, round, green-brown, weakly foliate

**Leaves:** basal rosettes, long-pointed, notched-serrate, lower leaves stalked, bare, green

**Flowers:** terminal, solitary, globular heads, deep blue — violet, petals turned inwards like claws, sometimes spiral appendages at tip; bracts lanceolate, narrow, pointed, green

**Flowering time:** May—September

**Habitat:** 800—2600 m, loamy, warm soils, meadows, pastures, wetlands, clearings, screes.
Quite frequent.

**Distribution:** Alps, Apennines, Pyrenees

# WOOD SCABIOUS

**Knautia dipsacifolia (= Scabiosa sylvatica)**

| | |
|---|---|
| **Family:** | Scabious Family Dipsacaceae |
| **Stem:** | 20—85 cm high, erect, strong, round, green, bare below, pubescent above, branching, foliate |
| **Leaves:** | in pairs, opposite, sessile, wide-lanceolate, serrate-crenate, green, reticulate, hairy, undivided |
| **Flowers:** | terminal, solitary on long stalks, heads 2.5—4 cm diameter, somewhat flattened, outmost florets larger than the inner ones, reddish violet, more rarely white, florets with five petals, four stamens, white or pink, calyx inconspicuous, green |
| **Flowering time:** | June—September |
| **Habitat:** | 400—2000 m, nutritious, loamy soils, edges of woods and bushes, clearings, gorges, banks of streams, mountain meadows. Quite frequent, gregarious. |
| **Distribution:** | Alps, Pyrenees |

Daisies near the Tajaspitze, Lechtal Alps, Tyrol

# ALPINE PASQUE FLOWER
## Pulsatilla alpina

| | |
|---|---|
| **Family:** | Buttercup Family Ranunculaceae |
| **Stem:** | 15—50 cm high, erect, green, slightly hairy, foliate |
| **Leaves:** | radical, stalked, three in number, divided, pinnate, green, three pinnate leaf bracts |
| **Flowers:** | terminal, solitary, 6—7 cm large, usually 6 petals, pure white, flushed a delicate bluish purple outside, hairy, surrounding numerous golden yellow stamens |
| **Fruit:** | bearded tuft of many long-haired styles (winged) |
| **Flowering time:** | May—July |
| **Habitat:** | 1500—2700 m, calcareous, mountain meadows, slopes, overgrown boulders, scrub, with alders. Not frequent. |

**Distribution:** Alps, Pyrenees, Apennines

---

**PROTECTED!**

---

# EDELWEISS

## Leontopodium alpinum

| | |
|---|---|
| **Family:** | Daisy Family Compositae |
| **Stem:** | 5—20 cm high, erect or ascending, round, green, white woolly hairs, foliate, frequently several from one root |
| **Leaves:** | basal rosettes, oblong-linear-lanceolate, green, entire, white woolly hairs; stem leaflets alternate, lanceolate-linear, sessile, blunt, strong woolly hairs |
| **Flowers:** | in three to twelve small terminal heads, grey to yellowish brown, small, inconspicuous disc florets; flowerheads surrounded in star shape by lanceolate bracts, spreading, narrow, entire, different lengths, woolly white hairs |
| **Flowering time:** | July—September |
| **Habitat:** | 1800—3500 m, sunny, stony soils, rocks, crevices, high pastures, meadows, ridges.<br>Rather rare, locally gregarious. |
| **Distribution:** | Alps, Apennines, Pyrenees |

---

**PROTECTED!**

# LLOYDIA or SNOWDON LILY

## Lloydia serotina

**Family:** Lily Family Liliaceae

**Stem:** 5—10 cm high, erect, slender, green-brown, foliate, bare

**Leaves:** radical, frequently as long as the stem, narrow-linear, grassy, somewhat fleshy, green; usually two stem leaves, alternate, narrow-lanceolate, sessile, decurrent, light green

**Flowers:** terminal, solitary, approx. 1.5 cm in diameter, erect, six petals, ovate-oblong, funnel-shaped, white with three reddish veins, slightly yellow-brown at base inside and outside; six light yellow stamens, somewhat longer than style

**Flowering time:** July—August

**Habitat:** 2000—3000 m, humus, acid stony soils deficient in lime, damp spots in semi-shade, rocks, rocky strips, windy ridges, with dwarf shrubs, mossy grass. Isolated, absent in some areas.

**Distribution:** Alps

# WHITE FALSE HELLEBORINE
## Veratrum album

| | |
|---|---|
| **Family:** | Lily Family Liliaceae |
| **Stem:** | 40—140 cm high, erect, strong, green, foliate, hairy, branching above |
| **Leaves:** | alternate, encircling stalk, very large, wide-lanceolate, parallel veined, green |
| **Flowers:** | spiky on branches, too, short stalked, corolla with six petals, ovately pointed, spreading, greenish yellow to dull white, throat darker; calyx inconspicuous, stamens ochre yellow |
| **Flowering time:** | July—August |
| **Habitat:** | 800—2700 m, damp, loamy soils, pastures, meadows. Frequent. |
| **Distribution:** | Alps |
| **Note:** | entire plant extremely poisonous, mere contact leads to symptoms of poisoning. |

# BURNT ORCHID

## Orchis ustulata

| | |
|---|---|
| **Family:** | Orchid Family Orchidaceae |
| **Stem:** | 8—25 cm high, erect, strong, round, green, not branching, weakly foliate |
| **Leaves:** | radical, ovate, wide, pointed, grass green, somewhat fleshy, parallel veined; stem leaves lanceolate, sessile or decurrent, unspotted, keeled |
| **Flowers:** | dense conical spikes or rounded-off cylinders, florets 8—12 mm long, upper petals in a close helmet, three-lobed lip, side lobes projecting, central lobe long, white, notched, dark red spots, spur blunt, short, pointing down; top of spike seemingly dark purple due to buds, fragrant. |
| **Flowering time:** | May—June |
| **Habitat:** | 800—2000 m, calcareous soils, warm meadows, pastures, mountain fields. Infrequent. |

**Distribution:** Alps, Apennines, Pyrenees

---

### PROTECTED!

---

# WHITE CROCUS

## Crocus albiflorus

| | |
|---|---|
| **Family:** | Iris Family Iridaceae |
| **Stem:** | mock pedicel, tubular, joining petals to corm, 6—12 cm high, erect, white, mauve or violet, bare |
| **Leaves:** | emerging from the corm, the leaves surround the flower stalk, narrow-linear, grass-like, green with central white stripe, keeled, developing after flowering |
| **Flowers:** | solitary, erect, large, bell-shaped, six petals, spatulate, entire, white, mauve or violet, tapering downwards into a tubular stalk, three stamens, golden yellow, style three-lobed, orange to yellowish red; ovary beneath ground in spring, above in summer |
| **Flowering time:** | March—June (depending on snow conditions and altitude) |
| **Habitat:** | 700—2700 m, soils rich in humus, fields, mountain meadows, pastures. Very frequent, gregarious, very prolific locally. |
| **Distribution:** | Alps, Apennines, Pyrenees, Jura, Carpathians, Balkans |

# SPRING PASQUE FLOWER
## Pulsatilla vernalis

**Family:** Buttercup Family Ranunculaceae

**Stem:** up to 15 cm high, erect or ascending, strong, green, round, golden, furry, hairy, foliate

**Leaves:** radical, rosette-like, stalked, palmate, pinnate, green, hairy; leaves under-developed or not yet present at flowering time.
Three whorled bracts beneath flower, points long-linear, woolly hairs, green

**Flowers:** solitary, terminal, ovate-campanulate, spreading when in full bloom to 40—60 mm diameter, six petals, obovate-round, white inside, outside pink to violet, furry hairs, numerous yellow stamens

**Flowering time:** April—July

**Habitat:** 1000—3000 m, calcareous and siliceous soils, mountain meadows, pastures, fields and overgrown ridges. Somewhat rare.

**Distribution:** Alps, Pyrenees, Norway

---

### PROTECTED!

# ST. BRUNO'S LILY

## Paradisea liliastrum

| | |
|---|---|
| **Family:** | Lily Family Liliaceae |
| **Stem:** | 30—50 cm high, erect, strong, round, leafless, bare, unbranching, green |
| **Leaves:** | radical, almost as long as the stem, narrow, grass-like, green, standing erect, not grooved |
| **Flowers:** | one-sided racemes, few in flower at same time, funnel-shaped, large, approx. 5 cm diameter, long petal points, pure white, on short stalks from leaf axils; small, lanceolate bracts, buds erect, flowers later nodding slightly; style somewhat longer than the six golden yellow stamens |
| **Flowering time:** | June—July |
| **Habitat:** | 800—2400 m, calcareous, nutritious loamy soils, fond of warmth, on mountain fields, pastures, open bushes, stony slopes, with green elders. Gregarious, but rare and absent in many areas. |
| **Distribution:** | Alps, Pyrenees, Apennines (southern and northern limestone Alps) |

# SWISS ROCK-JASMINE

### Androsace helvetica

| | |
|---|---|
| **Family:** | Primrose Family Primulaceae |

Dense, semi-spherical cushions, silvery grey — green, with small tile-like leafed branches, the plant grows very slowly and reaches an unusually great age, not infrequently up to 60 years.

**Leaves:** tile-like on the tiny branches, rosettes, very small, green, dense woolly hairs, giving a silvery appearance

**Flowers:** terminal, short stalked, flat spreading corolla out of the leaf axils, five petals, obovate, round, 4—6 mm in diameter, white with yellow eye, at the main flowering time the semi-spherical cushion is densely covered with florets

**Flowering time:** May—July

**Habitat:** 1800—3500 m, calcareous soils, rocks, fine crevices; its marvellous adaptability enables this plant to survive many decades of severest weather conditions.
Scattered, absent in some areas of the eastern limestone Alps.

**Distribution:** Alps (north-west limestone Alps and Dolomites)

---

**ENTIRELY PROTECTED!**

# STEMLESS CARLINE THISTLE

## *Carlina acaulis*

**Family:** Daisy Family Asteraceae

**Stem:** 5—25 cm high, erect, prostrate or ascending, round, green, brownish red tinged, foliate

**Leaves:** rosettes, pinnate, spiny toothed, narrow, long, stiff, dark green, brownish red tinged at the base; lobes pinnate, extremely sharp

**Flowers:** terminal, single heads, flat flowerhead 6—12 cm large, tubular florets brownish above, whitish beneath, secreting nectar, surrounded by silvery white, narrow-lanceolate parchment-like bracts which open in the sun and close in the rain

**Flowering time:** July—September

**Habitat:** up to 2800 m, poor soils in meadows and pastures, sometimes in the grass, on calcareous, stony ground, open woodland, gregarious. Quite frequent.

**Distribution:** Alps, Pyrenees, Apennines

---

**PROTECTED!**

# MOUNTAIN AVENS

## Dryas octopetala

**Family:** Rose Family Rosaceae

**Stem:** 5—12 cm high, erect, slender, round, brown-red, glandular hairs

**Leaves:** radical, stalked, lanceolate, notched, green, shiny above, silvery white downy beneath, length of leaf 3—6 cm, width of leaf 10—20 mm

**Flowers:** solitary, terminal, flower diameter 3—5 cm, eight petals, ovate-oblong, blunt, white, numerous stamens, golden yellow

**Flowering time:** May—August

**Habitat:** 800—2400 m, calcareous, stony soils, mountain meadows, detritus, overgrown boulders, wetlands, moraines, silted up areas, pioneer plant.
Quite frequent, gregarious.

**Distribution:** Alps, Apennines, Pyrenees, Norway

# PANICULATE or LIVELONG SAXIFRAGE

## Saxifraga paniculata

| | |
|---|---|
| **Family:** | Saxifrage Family Saxifragaceae |
| **Stem:** | 10—35 cm high, erect or ascending, round, ramose, slender, brownish red; weakly foliate, glandular hairy, sometimes cushion-like |
| **Leaves:** | rosettes, small, linear, blunt, toothed, green, lime encrusted at edges; stem leaves isolated, alternate, small, glandular, green |
| **Flowers:** | dense panicles, florets small, approx. 6—12 mm diameter, five petals, inversely spatulate, rayed out, yellowish white, some purple spotted; short, golden yellow stamens |
| **Flowering time:** | June—August |
| **Habitat:** | up to 3000 m, rocks, boulders, stony places, moraines.<br>Quite frequent. |

**Distribution:** Alps, Pyrenees, Apennines

---

**PROTECTED!**

---

# ALPINE MOON DAISY

## Leucanthemopsis alpina

| | |
|---|---|
| **Family:** | Daisy Family Compositae |
| **Stem:** | 6—15 cm high, erect, green, slender, foliate, somewhat angular, turf-forming root |
| **Leaves:** | radical, stalked, deeply pinnate, lower stem leaves cuneate, three-toothed, green, upper leaves narrow-lanceolate, sessile, entire, slender |
| **Flowers:** | solitary, terminal, large 3—4 cm diameter, white, linear ray florets surrounding golden yellow disc florets, semi-spherical, green, dark edged bracts |
| **Flowering time:** | July—August |
| **Habitat:** | 1800—3200 m, siliceous soils, shaly rock, fine detritus, moraines, snowy valleys, screes, pastures. In groups, but not frequent. |
| **Distribution:** | Alps, Pyrenees |

# Botany in brief

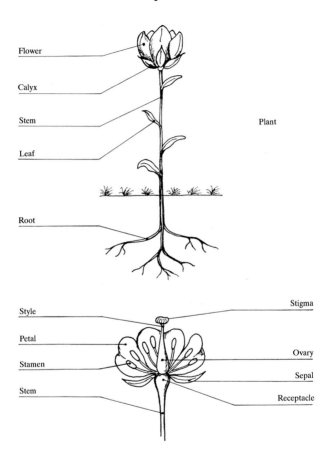

Flower

Calyx

Stem

Leaf

Root

Plant

Style

Petal

Stamen

Stem

Stigma

Ovary

Sepal

Receptacle

## STEM

branching

with knodes

angular

sulcate

erect

prostrate

ascending

## PHYLLOTAXIS

rosette

alternate

opposite

verticillate
whorled

## LEAF ARRANGEMENT

stalked

sessile

encircling stalk

— grooved

— decurrent

— bracts
— leaf axil
— stem leaves
— radical leaves
— rosette

215

# LEAF FORMS

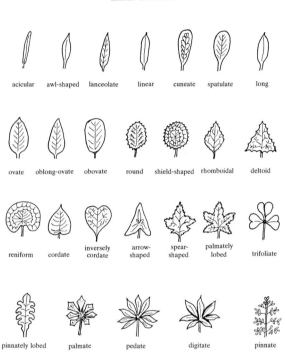

acicular · awl-shaped · lanceolate · linear · cuneate · spatulate · long

ovate · oblong-ovate · obovate · round · shield-shaped · rhomboidal · deltoid

reniform · cordate · inversely cordate · arrow-shaped · spear-shaped · palmately lobed · trifoliate

pinnately lobed · palmate · pedate · digitate · pinnate

unevenly pinnate · evenly pinnate

## LEAF MARGINS

entire

serrate

doubly serrate

dentate,
toothed

serrate-dentate

spiny-toothed

notched,
crenate

sinuate

runcinate

## VENATION

feathered

reticulate

parallel veined

## CALYX

tubular

ventricose

dialysepalous

inflated

two-lipped

veined

epicalyx

with scale

# INFLORESCENCES

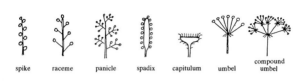

| spike | raceme | panicle | spadix | capitulum | umbel | compound umbel |

## CYMES

| whorl | dichasium | corymb | corymb-thyrsus | fascicle |

capitulum

flower-head

# FLOWER

ray floret

disc floret

ray florets outside
disc florets inside

nodding

with throat

flat

dialypetalous

campanulate,
bell-shaped

labiate

violet

ray florets
disc florets

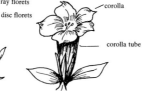
corolla

corolla tube

centre

# PETAL

entire

notched

deeply fringed

fringed

# ORCHIDS

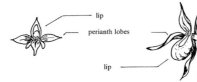
lip

perianth lobes

lip

219

# INDEX
## (alphabetically ordered)

221

223